TRINITY REPERTOIRE LIBRAI

the electronic keyboard collection book 1

Selected and edited by Jeremy Ward

Faber Music Bloomsbury House 74–77 Great Russell Street London WC1B 3DA
in association with
Trinity Guildhall 89 Albert Embankment London SE1 7TP

Contents

First published in 2005 by Faber Music Ltd
in association with Trinity College London
Bloomsbury House 74–77 Great Russell Street London WC1B 3DA
Cover design by Sue Clarke
Music processed by Jackie Leigh
Printed in England by Caligraving Ltd

ISBN10: 0-571-52221-1
EAN13: 978-0-571-52221-7

To buy Faber Music or Trinity publications or to find out about the full range of titles available please contact your local music retailer or Faber Music sales enquiries:

Faber Music Ltd, Burnt Mill, Elizabeth Way, Harlow CM20 2HX
Tel: +44 (0)1279 82 89 82 Fax: +44 (0)1279 82 89 83
sales@fabermusic.com www.fabermusicstore.com www.trinityguildhall.co.uk

Polovtsian Dance

Alexander Borodin (arr. Ward)

Voice: Oboe
Style: Ballad

The oboe needs to sound confident; play the eighth notes (quavers) and the *piano* section smoothly and remember where the oboist would breathe ('). Try adding a dual voice (strings) on the repeat to add colour, and possibly an accompaniment B.

Skip to my Lou

Traditional (arr. Ward)

Voice: Own Choice
Style: Own Choice

Choose your own voice, style and dynamic for this American tune. Banjo or fiddle with a bluegrass style, or clarinet with a jive style would suit well. For a more contemporary feel you could try guitar with rock style, or synth with ballad style. Experiment further by changing registers and rhythms.

Swinging Slippers!

Pam Wedgwood

Voice: Alto Sax Style: Swing

The alto sax suits the style of this piece well with its husky low register (at the beginning), and brighter tone higher up (in the middle section). Make sure the tied notes are held for the correct length and try adding some fills in the bar rests to add to the excitement. Consider what additions you could make on the D.S.

Coppélia

Léo Delibes (arr. Ward)

Voice: Strings Style: Viennese Waltz

The strings voice gives a full and luxurious sound; imagine the violins and cellos using long, sweeping bows to achieve the flowing *legato* phrases. You might like to add a harmony setting on the repeat.

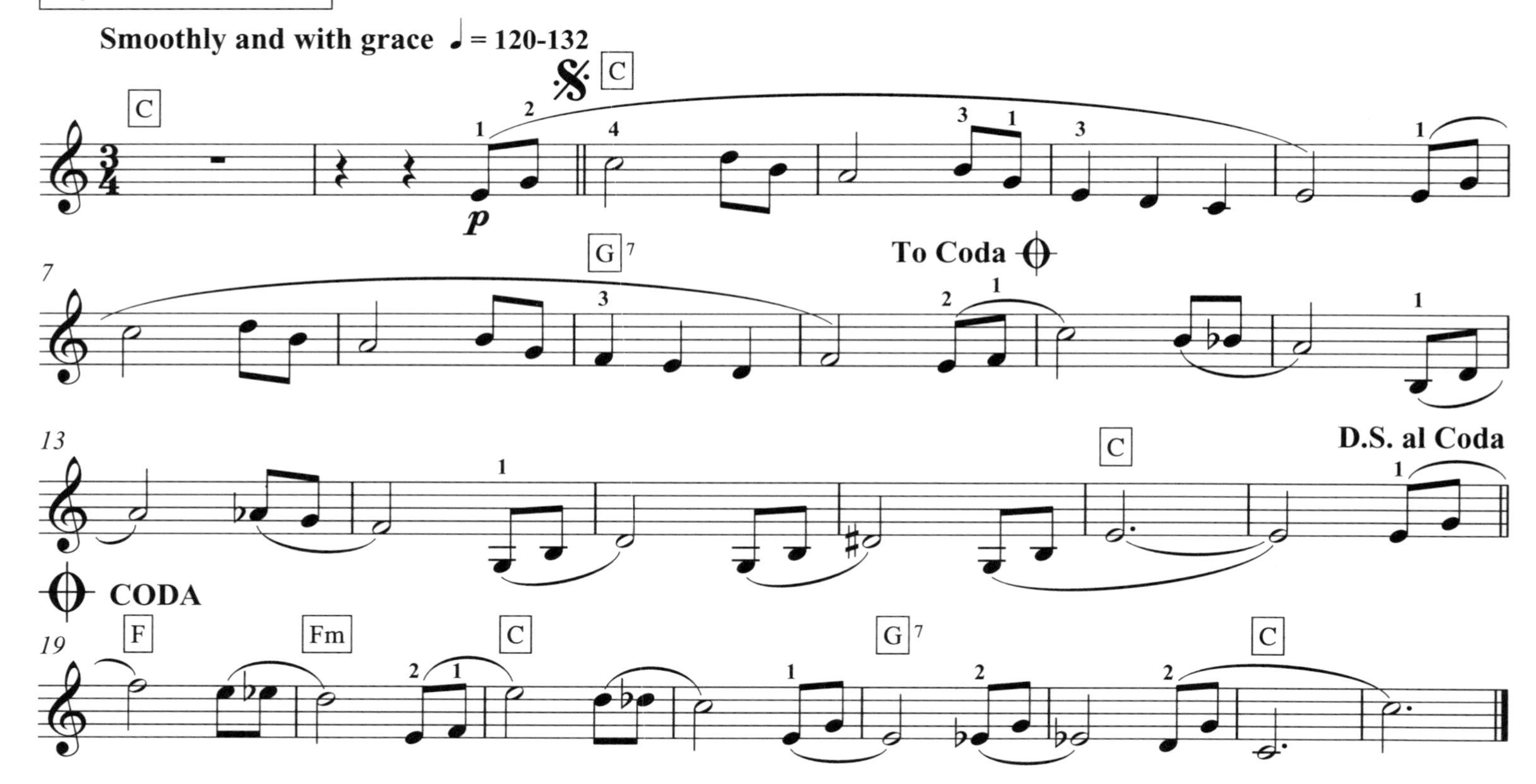

Tango for Trampoline

Elissa Milne

Voice: Clarinet Style: Tango

A tango is a sultry dance and the clarinet voice creates a great atmosphere. The *staccato* notes are the bouncing and the *legato* notes are the landing and rolling on the trampoline. The eighth note (quaver) rests are important: imagine taking a quick breath before bouncing. The clarinet player tongues the *staccatos* sharply at the end, as you jump off the trampoline!

War of the Galaxies

Composition project

Voice: Own Choice Style: Own Choice

You need to select a voice and style and also add some ideas to make this piece complete. The music is based on a film about space, so would suit a synth voice and a busy style. The opening idea is the theme of battle; develop it by adding a dual voice or harmony. The second idea is the theme of the earth and has a broader, more settled feel.

Don Giovanni

'La ci darem la mano'

Wolfgang Amadeus Mozart (arr. Ward)

Voice: Bassoon
Style: Children's March

Use any march if you don't have a Children's March style. The quarter notes (crotchets) should be short and bouncy to reflect the fun bassoon sound; remember that the player would need to breathe at the end of phrases. Try starting the piece with rhythm only, and putting the theme up an octave when you repeat it.

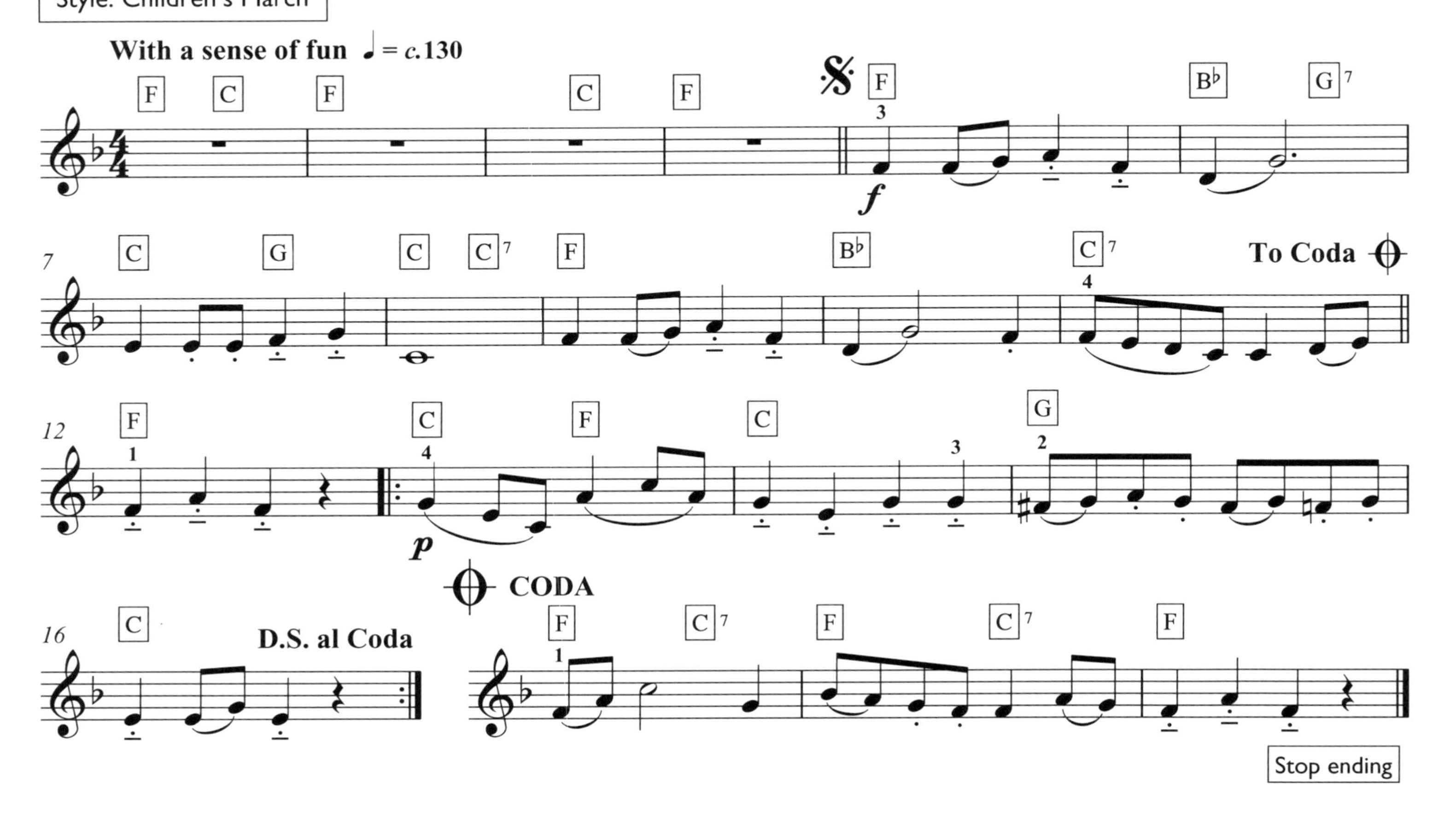

Scarborough Fair

Traditional (arr. Ward)

Voice: Own Choice
Style: Own Choice

You need to choose your own voice, style and dynamics and experiment with developing the material in this piece. Choose a voice that can sustain the long lyrical phrases and try adding a dual voice, varying the octave and making rhythmic changes. This traditional song was a hit for Simon and Garfunkel, so you could keep the folk feel (perhaps with a harp voice) or you could give it a more modern sound, perhaps with guitar.

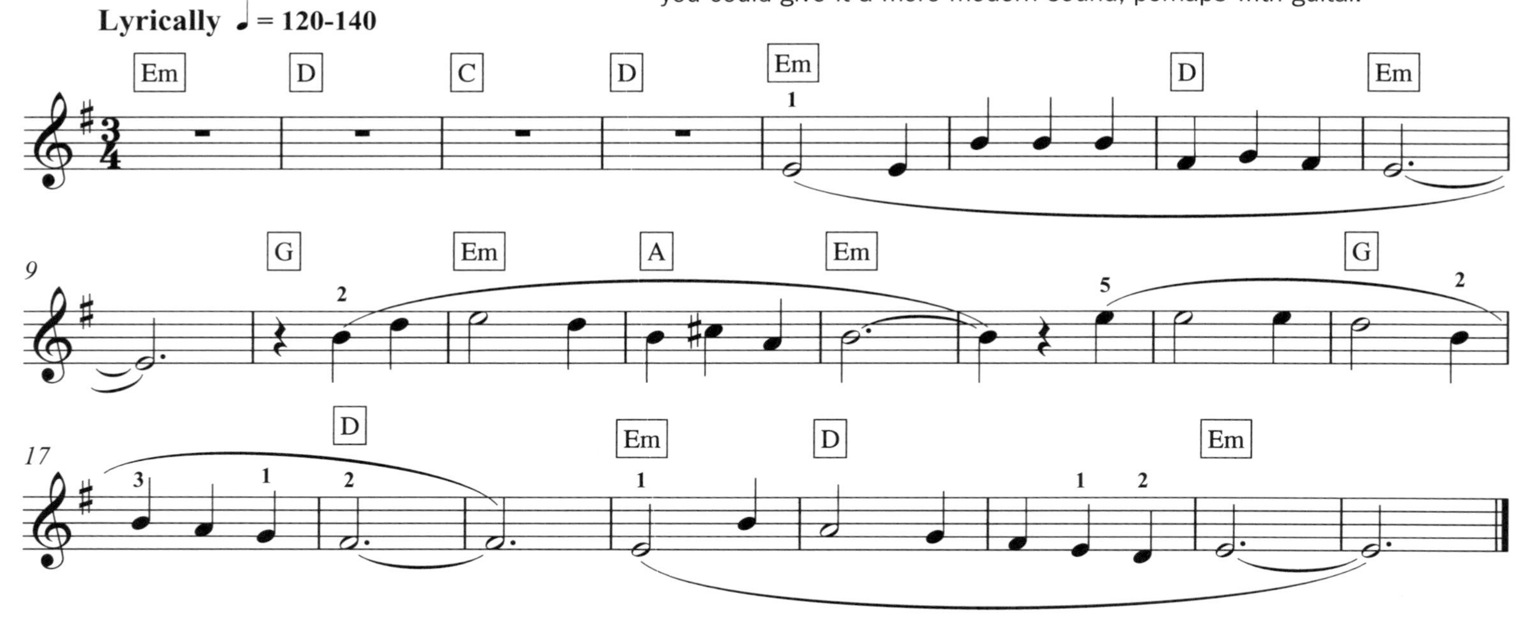

Sunset

Jeremy Ward

Voice: Any synth sound Style: Ballad

For this sunset over a beautiful view choose any synth sound that has a good sustained quality. The opening is calm; count the long notes carefully. Try a change of octave or a dual voice on the repeated section. The tune is stronger when it reappears, as if the colours are getting redder, so add another accompaniment level. The ending gets lower and softer as the sun disappears: take off the dual voice and go back to the initial accompaniment level. Use the fade in the last bar if you have one.

Folk Dance

Jeremy Ward

This is a concert piece which will get everyone applauding! It should flow smoothly, but do emphasise the beginnings of phrases. Make sure the melody line is secure before you add the grace notes. The minor section should sound a little calmer – but not for long, as it rises up to a grand ending.

Voice: Small Accordion
Style: Country

Music of the Night

Music by Andrew Lloyd Webber (arr. Ward)
Lyrics by Charles Hart
Additional lyrics by Richard Stilgoe

Voice: Strings
Style: Ballad (Slow 'n' easy)

This famous tune from 'Phantom of the Opera' is a love song, so phrase the music as if you were singing it. The opening should sound very free and the first section calm and smooth. The tension mounts in the second section, with the top notes in each phrase getting higher. You could add a dual voice in this section, but remember to take it off when the melody returns.

Alouette

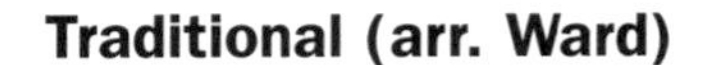
Traditional (arr. Ward)

Voice: Own Choice
Style: Own Choice

For this piece you need to choose the voice, style and dynamic and develop the material in some way. This French folk song would suit an accordion voice and bright style such as 8-beat pop, but try different effects such as synth voice and a modern dance style as well. Think about using dotted rhythms, changing the octaves, and perhaps starting without accompaniment.

Swan Lake

Legato - smoothly.

Pyotr Ilyich Tchaikovsky (arr. Ward)

Voice: Harp/Strings
Style: Ballad

♩ = practice 75

Swan Lake is a ballet, so this graceful piece needs to be played *legato*. You could add strings from bar 11 to add colour and a feeling of growth. For the D.S. try adding accompaniment B but remember to keep it *legato*.

Trumpet Trip

Jeremy Ward

Voice: Trumpet Style: Bossa Nova

This light-hearted piece was written with a TV game show in mind. The articulation is very important: imagine how clearly a trumpeter would tongue or slur the notes. The fills in the middle section should use another instrument (guitar or percussion) and it needs to build to the D.S. where you can add another accompaniment level. An automatic ending could work well here.

Soulful Sax

Jeremy Ward

Voice: Tenor Sax/Strings
Style: Swing

Remember to swing the eighth notes (quavers) in this piece and count the long tied notes carefully. The second section starts softly but the last two bars before the D.S. should feel as if they are building: try adding another accompaniment level and emphasise the upper notes. An auto ending could be effective.

Chicken Reel

Traditional (arr. Ward)

Voice: Banjo
Style: Bluegrass

This piece is a country dance and the choice of banjo captures the style. Banjo notes don't last very long and sound best in the higher register, which suits this fast, showy piece. Accent the D sharp quarter note (crotchet) at the beginning of each phrase, and make sure the quarter notes (crotchets) are light and separated in the repeated section.

Caribbean Holiday

Composition project

Voice: Own Choice
Style: Own Choice

You need to select a voice, style and dynamics and compose some bars to make this piece complete. The title will give you ideas: think about tuned percussion such as steel drums. For the new bars, don't try to compose different ideas: if the chord sequence is the same, use ideas from the previous phrase by changing the octave, the rhythm or a few of the notes.

Tibetan Tune

Jeremy Ward

Voice: Shakuhachi Style: Acoustic Ballad or Light Waltz

This piece begins with an improvised feel – as if you are in the Himalayan mountains and you hear this across the valley. Try experimenting: play the first two bars unaccompanied and then add an A minor chord (but above the split, so still no accompaniment) until bar 9. When the auto accompaniment starts, keep the calm feeling: state the theme simply and play it an octave down on the repeat. Try adding a dual voice from bar 21. The ending uses the Shakuhachi tone qualities in all the registers; the last note should die away.

Knowing Me, Knowing You

Stig Anderson/Benny Andersson/
Bjoern Ulvaeus (arr. Ward)

Voice: DX Modern or any electric piano
Style: Hard Rock

Rhythmic precision is important here, as are the rests; don't rush the eighth notes (quavers). Experiment with accompaniments and dual voices: try introducing another sound at bar 24, and bars 30–33 would work well with brass or strings and up an octave when repeated. Try fading out at the end if you can.

Big Band Stand

Composition project

Voice: Own Choice
Style: Own Choice

Here is a piece for you to develop: you need to select a voice, style and dynamics as well as develop some musical ideas. The clue is in the title: use a big band voice and style. Try starting with just a rhythm for a couple of bars, then bring the chords in for the introduction. The use of harmony control would be useful here, as would a change in octave and use of accompaniment B on the D.S.